My First HANDWRITING Practice Pad

BLANK-LINED WORKBOOK FOR KIDS

AGES 3+

This Book Belongs to:

FOR A LITTLE INSPIRATION
follow along at:

◎ @JUNEANDLUCY

f @JUNEANDLUCY

WWW. JUNELUCY.COM

Shop our other books at
www.junelucy.com

Wholesale distribution through Ingram Content Group
www.ingramcontent.com/publishers/distribution/wholesale

For questions and customer service, email us at
support@junelucy.com

© June & Lucy. All rights reserved. No part of this publication may be reproduced, distributed, or transmitted, in any form or by any means, including photocopying, recording, or other electronic or mechanical methods, without prior written permission of the publisher, except in the case of brief quotations embodied in critical reviews and certain other noncommercial uses permitted by copyright law.

Manufactured by Amazon.ca
Bolton, ON

14622518R00061